Collections for Young Scholars™

READING/WRITING CONNECTION

VOLUME 2

PROGRAM AUTHORS
Carl Bereiter
Valerie Anderson
Ann Brown
Marlene Scardamalia
Joe Campione

CONSULTING AUTHORS
Michael Pressley
Iva Carruthers
Bill Pinkney

OPEN COURT PUBLISHING COMPANY
CHICAGO AND PERU, ILLINOIS

Dialogue

In "Dragons and Giants," Arnold Lobel uses dialogue to tell us what the characters are saying and doing. Find more examples of dialogue in the story. Write down the examples you find.

Page: _____

Example: _____

_____

Page: _____

Example: _____

_____

Page: _____

Example: _____

_____

Page: _____

Example: _____

_____

Use this page when you want to use dialogue in your own writing.

Name

Sentence Types

Look through "Dragons and Giants" for examples of sentences that **tell**, sentences that **ask**, and sentences that show **strong emotion**. Write the example and the kind of sentence it is.

Example: _____

_____

Sentence type: _____

Example: _____

_____

Sentence type: _____

Example: _____

_____

Sentence type: _____

Example: _____

_____

Sentence type: _____

Look at this page for types of sentences you might use when writing stories. Make sure you use the correct end mark.

Sentence Types

Being Brave/Unit 1

Name

Characterization

Look through *The Hole in the Dike* or other stories you have read to find examples of how the writer tells the readers what a character is like. Write down the examples you find. Does the example tell something the character did, said, or thought? Write what each example tells about the character.

Story: _____ Page: _____

Character: _____

Example: _____

_____

What this tells about the character: _____

_____

Story: _____ Page: _____

Character: _____

Example: _____

_____

What this tells about the character: _____

_____

Use this page when you want to tell readers what a character is like in your own writing.

Giving Opinions

In *Molly the Brave and Me* the author uses opinions
to tell readers what a character thinks about another
character in the story. Look through the story to find
more examples of what a character thinks about
another character. Write down the examples you find.
Write the opinion and who has the opinion.

Page: _____

Opinion: _____

_____

_____

_____

Who has the opinion? _____

_____

Page: _____

Opinion: _____

_____

_____

_____

Who has the opinion? _____

_____

Copyright © 1995 Open Court Publishing Company

Elaboration

Name

Dialogue

In *Molly the Brave and Me* the author uses dialogue to tell us what the characters are saying to each other. Find examples of dialogue in the story or in other stories you have read. Write down the examples. Then circle the word or words that tell who is speaking.

Story: _____ Page: _____

Example of dialogue: _____

_____

_____

Story: _____ Page: _____

Example of dialogue: _____

_____

_____

Story: _____ Page: _____

Example of dialogue: _____

_____

_____

Use this page when you want to use dialogue in your own writing.

Name _____

Biography

Name

A biography is a story about a real person's life. *Sally Ride, Astronaut: An American First* is a biography because it tells facts about a real person's life. It also tells what makes her interesting and important. Look through the story and find more examples of facts and information that tell about Sally Ride and the things she did. Write down the examples you find and tell what makes Sally Ride interesting.

Facts about Sally Ride's life: _____

_____

_____

_____

_____

What makes Sally Ride interesting or important? _____

_____

_____

_____

Give one reason why authors write biographies: _____

_____

Use this page when writing a true story about a real person.

Genre
_____

Being Brave/Unit 1

Writing Paragraphs

Find examples of paragraphs that tell a lot about something in *Sally Ride, Astronaut: An American First* or in other stories you have read. Write the main idea of the paragraph.

Story: _____ Page: _____

The main idea: _____

_____

Story: _____ Page: _____

The main idea: _____

_____

Story: _____ Page: _____

The main idea: _____

_____

Story: _____ Page: _____

The main idea: _____

_____

Name _____

Fairy Tale

"The Three Wishes" is a fairy tale. Look through the story again. Write down any characteristics of a fairy tale that you find.

Page: _____ Characteristic: _____

_____

_____

Page: _____ Characteristic: _____

_____

_____

Page: _____ Characteristic: _____

_____

_____

Remember to use these fairy-tale characteristics when writing a fairy tale.

Genre

Point of View

The author of "The Three Wishes" wrote the story from the narrator's point of view. Look at this story or other stories that you have read and find words that let you know who is telling the story. Tell why these words are clues.

Page: _____ Clue words: _____

Why are these words clues? _____

_____

Page: _____ Clue words: _____

Why are these words clues? _____

_____

Page: _____ Clue words: _____

Why are these words clues? _____

_____

Page: _____ Clue words: _____

Why are these words clues? _____

_____

Point of View

Dialogue

Authors use dialogue, or the exact words characters say, to make their stories come alive. Look through the stories you have read in this unit or in other units. Find examples of dialogue. Write them on the lines below. Then write the name of the character who is speaking.

Page: _____ Example: _____

_____

_____

Character's name: _____

Page: _____ Example: _____

_____

_____

Character's name: _____

Page: _____ Example: _____

_____

_____

Character's name: _____

Remember to add dialogue to stories you are writing.

Name

Descriptive Words

Authors pick their words very carefully to help the reader better picture the story. Look through this story and the first story in the unit. Find and write descriptive words. Then tell whether they answer the questions *what kind? which one?* or *how much?*

Page: _____ Descriptive word: _____

What question does the word answer? _____

_____

Page: _____ Descriptive word: _____

What question does the word answer? _____

_____

Page: _____ Descriptive word: _____

What question does the word answer? _____

_____

Page: _____ Descriptive word: _____

What question does the word answer? _____

_____

Sentence Types

Look through *The Empty Pot* or other stories that
you have read. Find examples of sentences that tell,
ask, or show strong emotion. Fill in the blanks below.

Sentence: _____

_____

Type: _____

Sentence: _____

_____

Type: _____

Sentence: _____

_____

Type: _____

Variety in Writing

Setting

Stories are set in many interesting places—from castles to playgrounds. Look through *The Empty Pot* or other stories. Find examples of setting. Write down each example and write how the author describes the setting.

Story: _____

Setting: _____

How the author describes the setting: _____

_____

Story: _____

Setting: _____

How the author describes the setting: _____

_____

Story: _____

Setting: _____

How the author describes the setting: _____

_____

Think of interesting settings you might like to write about. Add these ideas to your Writer's Notebook.

Story Elements

Plot

Authors often plan their stories before writing. Look
through *Cinderella* or another story in this unit. List
the characters and the important events in the story.
Then fill in the plot line on the next page.

Main Characters

_____

_____

_____

_____

Important Events in the Story

_____

_____

_____

_____

_____

_____

_____

_____

Name

Story Elements

Plot continued

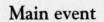

Main event

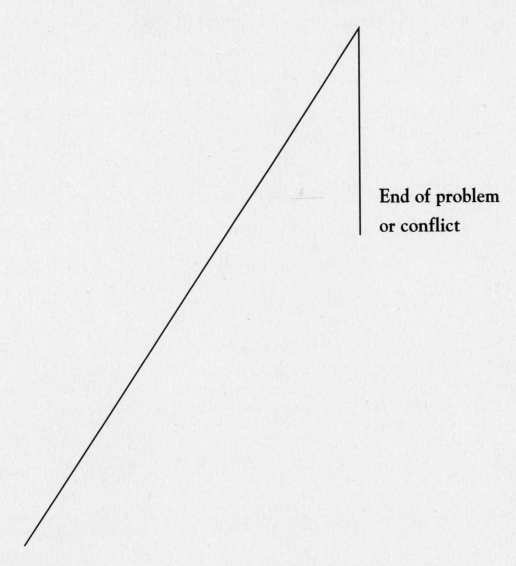

**End of problem
or conflict**

Characters

Setting

Problem

Check stories you have written for these important
story parts.

Name

Writing Paragraphs

Look through *Cinderella* or other stories for good paragraphs. Tell what the paragraph is about. If you find a sentence that states the main idea, write it down. If not, write the main idea in your own words.

Page: _____

What paragraph is about: _____

_____

Main idea: _____

_____

Page: _____

What paragraph is about: _____

_____

Main idea: _____

_____

Page: _____

What paragraph is about: _____

_____

Main idea: _____

_____

Writing Paragraphs

Problems and Solutions

Authors often make their stories more exciting by giving their characters problems to solve. Look through "Amadou's Story" or other stories that you have read. List problems that story characters have and tell their solutions.

Story: _____

Problem: _____

_____

Solution: _____

_____

Story: _____

Problem: _____

_____

Solution: _____

_____

Name

Expressing Characters' Thoughts and Feelings

Authors tell about their characters in many ways. Look through "Amadou's Story" or other stories that you have read. Find examples that tell characters' thoughts or feelings. Tell what the thought or feeling is.

Story: _____ Page: _____

Thought or feeling: _____

_____

_____

_____

Story: _____ Page: _____

Thought or feeling: _____

_____

_____

_____

Story: _____ Page: _____

Thought or feeling: _____

_____

_____

_____

Characterization

Rich and Poor/Unit 2

Name

Adjectives

Look through "The Golden Goose" or other stories. Find and write words that describe. Tell what person or thing the words describe.

Story: _____ Page: _____

Word or words that describe: _____

_____

Person or thing described: _____

_____

Story: _____ Page: _____

Word or words that describe: _____

_____

Person or thing described: _____

_____

Story: _____ Page: _____

Word or words that describe: _____

_____

Person or thing described: _____

_____

Story Beginnings and Endings

Look through "The Golden Goose" and other stories
in this unit. Tell what information is given in the
beginnings and in the endings.

Story: _____

Beginning page: _____

Information given: _____

_____

_____

Ending page: _____

Information given: _____

_____

_____

Story: _____

Beginning page: _____

Information given: _____

_____

_____

Ending page: _____

Information given: _____

_____

_____

Name

Story Elements

Rich and Poor/Unit 2

Giving Explanations

Sometimes authors give explanations or step-by-step details about something that happens. In *Fossils Tell of Long Ago*, the author gives many explanations to help the reader understand the different ways in which fossils are formed. Find examples of explanations of how something happens in this story or in any other story you have read. Write a sentence or two telling what the explanation is about.

Story: _____ Page: _____

What is being explained? _____

_____

_____

Story: _____ Page: _____

What is being explained? _____

_____

_____

Story: _____ Page: _____

What is being explained? _____

_____

_____

Name

Elaboration

Giving Definitions

Sometimes authors use definitions to tell the
meaning of words that are important in their writing.
The author of *Fossils Tell of Long Ago* gives definitions
of words in the story to help the reader understand
important ideas quickly. Find examples of definitions
in this story or in any other stories you have read.
Write the word and the definition given in the story.

Story: _____ Page: _____

Word: _____

Definition: _____

_____

Story: _____ Page: _____

Word: _____

Definition: _____

_____

Story: _____ Page: _____

Word: _____

Definition: _____

_____

Elaboration

Descriptions

Authors often give descriptions of persons, places, or things. Descriptions help the reader picture what the author is writing about. Find examples of descriptions in this story or in any other stories that you have read. Write the description. Then name the thing that is being described.

Story: _____ Page: _____

Description: _____

_____

_____

_____

Thing being described: _____

_____

Story: _____ Page: _____

Description: _____

_____

_____

_____

Thing being described: _____

_____

Copyright © 1995 Open Court Publishing Company

Description

Questions

A good way for a writer to present ideas about a subject is to ask questions and then give possible answers in his or her article. Possible answers are called **conjectures.** Find examples of questions and conjectures in "Why Did the Dinosaurs Disappear?" Write the questions below. Then write the conjectures or the important ideas in your own words.

Page: _____

Question: _____

_____

Conjecture or idea: _____

_____

_____

_____

Page: _____

Question: _____

_____

Conjecture or idea: _____

_____

_____

_____

Questions

Name

Time and Order Words

Words like *today* and *now* tell you when something is happening. Words such as *first* and *next* tell the order in which things take place. Find examples of words and phrases used to show time or order in "Why Did the Dinosaurs Disappear?" or in any other stories that you have read. Write the words or phrases below.

Story: _____

Words Used to Show Time	**Words Used to Show Order**
_____	_____
_____	_____
_____	_____
_____	_____

Story: _____

Words Used to Show Time	**Words Used to Show Order**
_____	_____
_____	_____
_____	_____
_____	_____

Name

Indicators of Time and Order

Time and Order

Words like *yesterday*, *now*, and *soon* tell you when something is happening. Words such as *first*, *then*, and *next* help explain the order in which things take place. In *The Elves and the Shoemaker*, and any other stories you have read, find words and phrases that show time and order.

Time

_____

_____

_____

_____

Order

_____

_____

_____

_____

Indicators of Time and Order

Sentence Types

In *The Elves and the Shoemaker*, the author uses three different kinds of sentences to make his writing interesting. Find examples of each of these kinds of sentences in stories you have read. Remember to use all three kinds in your own writing.

Sentence that tells: _____

_____

Story: _____ Page: _____

_____

Sentence that asks: _____

_____

Story: _____ Page: _____

_____

Sentence that shows emotion: _____

_____

Story: _____ Page: _____

_____

Name

Sentence Types continued

Sentence that tells: _____

_____

Story: _____ Page: _____

_____

Sentence that asks: _____

_____

Story: _____ Page: _____

_____

Sentence that shows emotion: _____

_____

Story: _____ Page: _____

_____

Interesting Verbs

Verbs are words that describe action. Good writers use interesting verbs to help form a clear picture for their readers of what is happening in their stories. Write down some interesting verbs from *Mushroom in the Rain* and other stories you have read. Try using some of these verbs in your own writing.

Interesting Verb	Story, Page Number

Fantasy

In fantasy stories, strange and curious things happen. Fantasies include both things that are real and things that are **make-believe**. Take another look at *Mushroom in the Rain* and other fantasies you have read and find what was real and what was make-believe.

Story: _____

Real: _____

_____

_____

Make-believe: _____

_____

_____

Story: _____

Real: _____

_____

_____

Make-believe: _____

_____

_____

Genre

Giving Reasons

Writers give reasons to make their ideas clear to readers and to give readers answers to things they may wonder about. The reasons in a story may tell **why something happened, why something is the way it is,** or **why characters feel the way they do**. Find examples from "The Camel's Nose," or from other stories you have read, where the author gives reasons that answer the question *Why?*

Story: _____ Page: _____

Why? question: _____

_____

Reason(s) that explains why: _____

_____

_____

Story: _____ Page: _____

Why? question: _____

_____

Reason(s) that explains why: _____

_____

_____

Elaboration

Name

Characterization

Writers help readers learn about their characters by showing how the characters **act** and by telling what the characters **say, think,** and **feel.** Find clues the author gives that show you what the characters are like in *Corduroy,* or in any other stories that you have read.

Story: _____

Character: _____

What the character is like: _____

_____

_____

Clues the author gives that make you think this: _____

_____

_____

Story: _____

Character: _____

What the character is like: _____

_____

_____

Clues the author gives that make you think this: _____

_____

_____

Characterization

34 R/WC

Name

Words that Show Place

In order to tell readers **where something is** or to help readers **picture where events are happening** in a story, authors use words and phrases like *under, on top of,* and *inside*. Find examples of such words and phrases in *Corduroy*, or in any other stories you have read, that help you picture what the author is describing.

Story: _____

Words and phrases that show place

_____   _____

_____   _____

_____   _____

Story: _____

Words and phrases that show place

_____   _____

_____   _____

_____   _____

Story: _____

Words and phrases that show place

_____   _____

_____   _____

_____   _____

Indicators of Place and Location

Name

Headings

Writers sometimes use headings to break up their stories into smaller parts, which are easier to read. Find examples from *Clara Barton: Red Cross Pioneer* and other stories you have read where the headings helped you as you read.

Story: _____

Heading: _____

What information is included under the heading? _____

_____

_____

_____

_____

Story: _____

Heading: _____

What information is included under the heading? _____

_____

_____

_____

_____

Name

Writing Paragraphs

Find paragraphs in *Clara Barton: Red Cross Pioneer*, or in other stories you have read, that tell a lot about something. Write what the paragraph is about. Then write the details the author gives to tell more about this idea.

Story: _____ Page: _____

What does the paragraph tell about? _____

_____

_____

Details the author gives about that idea: _____

_____

_____

_____

Story: _____ Page: _____

What does the paragraph tell about? _____

_____

_____

Details the author gives about that idea: _____

_____

_____

_____

Writing Paragraphs

Giving Reasons

Writers give reasons to make their ideas clear to readers or to give readers answers to things they may wonder about. Find examples from *Music, Music for Everyone*, or from other stories you have read, where the author gives reasons that answer the question *Why?*

Story: _____ Page: _____

Why? question: _____

_____

Reason(s) that explains why: _____

_____

_____

_____

Story: _____ Page: _____

Why? question: _____

_____

Reason(s) that explains why: _____

_____

_____

_____

Elaboration

Name

Strong Topic Sentences

Find examples from *Music, Music for Everyone* and other stories where the author uses strong topic sentences to tell what the paragraph is all about. Then write the details from the paragraph that tell about the main idea.

Story: _____ Page: _____

Main idea of the paragraph: _____

_____

Details given about the main idea: _____

_____

Story: _____ Page: _____

Main idea of the paragraph: _____

_____

Details given about the main idea: _____

_____

Story: _____ Page: _____

Main idea of the paragraph: _____

_____

Details given about the main idea: _____

_____

Name

Setting

Stories are set in many interesting places—from castles to playgrounds. In *A Pair of Red Clogs,* the author uses interesting details to help her readers picture the setting. Find parts in this and other stories you have read in which the author shows the time and the place of the action.

Story: _____

What is the setting of the story? _____

_____

What words give details of time and place? _____

_____

_____

Story: _____

What is the setting of the story? _____

_____

What words give details of time and place? _____

_____

_____

Think about exciting places where you might like your stories to take place. Add these ideas to your Writer's Notebook.

Story Elements

Expressing Characters' Thoughts and Feelings

Readers learn about the characters in a story by the characters' words and actions. They also learn about them through what the author says about their thoughts and feelings about events or other characters. Look through *A Pair of Red Clogs* or other stories that you have read. Find examples of ways in which the author lets you know a character's thoughts and feelings. Write the example. Tell how the author shows the character's thoughts and feelings.

Story: _____

Character's thoughts and feelings: _____

_____

How does the author show character's thoughts and feelings?

_____

_____

Story: _____

Character's thoughts and feelings: _____

_____

How does the author show character's thoughts and feelings?

_____

_____

Characterization

Sentence Types

In "The Pudding Like a Night on the Sea," Ann
Cameron uses different types of sentences. Find more
examples of sentence types in this or other stories.
Write them below with the correct punctuation.

Statements:

_____

_____

_____

_____

_____

_____

Questions:

_____

_____

_____

_____

_____

_____

Name

Sentence Types continued

Commands:

_____

_____

_____

_____

_____

_____

_____

Exclamations:

_____

_____

_____

_____

_____

_____

_____

Look in your writing folder. How many of these
sentence types have you used?

Name

Similes

Look in "The Pudding Like a Night on the Sea"
or other stories that you have read. Find and write
examples of similes. Write the two things that are
being compared.

Story: _____

Simile: _____

_____

Things being compared: _____

Story: _____

Simile: _____

_____

Things being compared: _____

Story: _____

Simile: _____

_____

Things being compared: _____

Using similes is a good way to describe something in
a new and interesting way. Look through your writing
folder. Add similes to improve your writing.

Name

Giving Causes

Look in "The Boy Who Cried Wolf" and other stories that you have read. Find sentences in which the author tells about an event. Look in the story for the cause of the event. Write the event and the cause.

Story: _____

Event: _____

_____

_____

Cause: _____

_____

Story: _____

Event: _____

_____

_____

Cause: _____

_____

Name

Elaboration

Characterization

Authors describe their characters by telling how they feel and what they think, say, and do. Look through *The Tale of Peter Rabbit* or other stories that you have read. Find and write words or phrases that tell something about a story character. Tell how the author describes the character.

Story character: _____

What character is like: _____

_____

_____

The author describes the character by _____

_____

_____

_____

Story character: _____

What character is like: _____

_____

_____

The author describes the character by _____

_____

_____

_____

Giving Reasons

Look through *The Tale of Peter Rabbit* or other stories that you have read. Find examples of reasons the author has given to explain an event or a character's action. Write each reason and the event or the action that it explains.

Story: _____

Reason: _____

_____

Event or action explained: _____

_____

Story: _____

Reason: _____

_____

Event or action explained: _____

_____

Story: _____

Reason: _____

_____

Event or action explained: _____

_____

Elaboration

Words That Show Place

Look through *The Tale of Peter Rabbit* or other stories that you have read. Find examples of words or phrases that show where the story takes place.

Story: _____

Words or phrases that show place: _____

_____

Story: _____

Words or phrases that show place: _____

_____

Story: _____

Words or phrases that show place: _____

_____

Story: _____

Words or phrases that show place: _____

_____

Story: _____

Words or phrases that show place: _____

_____

Indicators of Place

Responsibility/Unit 5

Name

Problems and Solutions

Stories are often exciting because the characters have to solve difficult problems. Look through "Three Hundred Spartans" or other stories that you have read. Find examples of problems. Write how the problem is solved. Discuss with your classmates how these problems and solutions make the story interesting to read.

Story: _____

Problem: _____

_____

Solution: _____

_____

Story: _____

Problem: _____

_____

Solution: _____

_____

Name

Giving Information About an Event

Authors give information about story events to help the reader understand the events better. Look through "Three Hundred Spartans" or other stories that you have read. Find examples of important story events. Write the information the author gives to tell about the event.

Story: _____

Event: _____

_____

Information given: _____

_____

_____

Story: _____

Event: _____

_____

Information given: _____

_____

_____

Look through your writing folder. Find descriptions of story events that you could improve by giving more information. Refer to this page for ideas.

Elaboration

Characterization

You have just read some ways in which Taro Yashima made his character interesting in *Crow Boy*. Find examples from this story, or from any other stories you have read, that show how the author makes the characters interesting. Copy sentences that help you know what a character is like.

Story: _____ Page: _____

Sentence showing what a character is like: _____

_____

_____

Story: _____ Page: _____

Sentence showing what a character is like: _____

_____

_____

Story: _____ Page: _____

Sentence showing what a character is like: _____

_____

_____

Characterization

Name

Giving Examples

In *Crow Boy*, the writer gives examples to help the reader understand an idea. Find some examples that make ideas clear in this story and in other stories you have read. Write them on the lines below.

Story: _____ Page: _____

Writer's idea that is explained: _____

_____

Examples given: _____

_____

Story: _____ Page: _____

Writer's idea that is explained: _____

_____

Examples given: _____

_____

Story: _____ Page: _____

Writer's idea that is explained: _____

_____

Examples given: _____

_____

Copyright © 1995 Open Court Publishing Company

Elaboration

Name

Plot

Find examples of important story events that make up the plot of any story you have read and would like to reread. First list the characters, then list in order the important events in the story. When you have done this, place the story events on the plot line on the next page.

Main characters: _____

_____

_____

Important events in the story: _____

_____

_____

_____

_____

_____

_____

_____

_____

_____

Story Elements

Plot continued

Name

Main Event

End of problem or conflict

Characters

Setting

Problem

Use this page when writing or revising your own stories.

Story Elements

Dialogue

In "The Foolish, Timid Rabbit," Ellen Babbitt used dialogue, or the exact words characters say, to make the story more interesting. Find examples of dialogue that tell about events in this story or other stories you have read. Write the title of the story and the example of dialogue that tells about the events in the story.

Story: _____ Page: _____

Dialogue that tells about an event: _____

_____

_____

Story: _____ Page: _____

Dialogue that tells about an event: _____

_____

_____

Story: _____ Page: _____

Dialogue that tells about an event: _____

_____

_____

Use this page when you want to use dialogue to tell about events in a story.

Name

Giving Explanations

In *How We Learned the Earth Is Round* or in any other selection you have read, find examples in which the writer uses explanations to make an idea clear. Write the idea in your own words, then write the explanation of the idea.

Selection: _____ Page: _____

Writer's idea that is being explained: _____

_____

Explanation of the idea: _____

_____

Selection: _____ Page: _____

Writer's idea that is being explained: _____

_____

Explanation of the idea: _____

_____

Selection: _____ Page: _____

Writer's idea that is being explained: _____

_____

Explanation of the idea: _____

_____

Elaboration

Writing Paragraphs

Find paragraphs in which you can tell the most
important idea. Look through *How We Learned the
Earth Is Round* or any other selection you have read.
Write down the most important idea. Then write what
all the sentences tell about.

Selection: _____ Page: _____

The most important idea in the paragraph: _____

_____

_____

What do all the sentences tell about? _____

_____

_____

Selection: _____ Page: _____

The most important idea in the paragraph: _____

_____

_____

What do all the sentences tell about? _____

_____

_____

Use this page when revising pieces in your writing folder.
Be sure that all the sentences in a paragraph go together.

Name

Using Descriptive Words

In *The Emperor's New Clothes*, and in other selections you have read, authors use adjectives to tell how something looks or how many of a thing there are. Find examples of words used to describe an object or event and list them below.

Selection: _____ Page: _____

Words used to describe (adjectives): _____

_____

_____

Selection: _____ Page: _____

Words used to describe (adjectives): _____

_____

_____

Selection: _____ Page: _____

Words used to describe (adjectives): _____

_____

_____

When you want to make the ideas clear in your writing, use this page for examples of words that describe.

Description

Expressing Characters' Opinions

Look for examples of characters' opinions (feelings or thoughts about something) in *The Emperor's New Clothes* or in any other story you have read. Copy a sentence or two that tells the character's opinion. Then tell whose opinion it is.

Selection: _____ Page: _____

Opinion: _____

_____

Character: _____

Selection: _____ Page: _____

Opinion: _____

_____

Character: _____

Selection: _____ Page: _____

Opinion: _____

_____

Character: _____

When writing or revising stories, use this page for examples of characters' opinions to make your writing clear.

Name

Giving Explanations

In *The First Americans*, the author gives explanations to help the reader understand an idea. In this story and in other stories you have read, find more explanations that make ideas clear. Write them on the lines below.

Story: _____ Page: _____

An explanation that helps make an idea clear: _____

_____

_____

_____

Story: _____ Page: _____

An explanation that helps make an idea clear: _____

_____

_____

_____

Story: _____ Page: _____

An explanation that helps make an idea clear: _____

_____

_____

_____

Name

Elaboration

Giving Examples

In *The First Americans*, the writer gives examples to help the reader understand an idea. In this story and in other stories you have read, find more examples that make ideas clear. Write them on the lines below.

Story: _____ Page: _____

An idea that is made clear: _____

_____

The examples given to help make the idea clear: _____

_____

_____

Story: _____ Page: _____

An idea that is made clear: _____

_____

The examples given to help make the idea clear: _____

_____

_____

Use this page when you want to use examples in your writing to make your ideas clearer.

Name

Elaboration

Using Words to Show Time and Order

Look through *Follow the Dream* or other stories you have read for words that show time and order. Write the name of the story and the word. Then draw a circle around the word *time* or the word *order* to tell what the word shows.

Name

Story: _____

Word: _____

Time   **Order**

Story: _____

Word: _____

Time   **Order**

Story: _____

Word: _____

Time   **Order**

Story: _____

Word: _____

Time   **Order**

When writing or revising stories, use this page to help you remember words that show time and order.

Indicators of Time and Order

Writing Paragraphs

In *Follow the Dream* and in other stories, find paragraphs that tell a lot about something. Write what all the sentences tell about. Then write the main idea of the paragraph.

Story: _____ Page: _____

What do all the sentences tell about? _____

_____

What is the main idea of the paragraph? _____

_____

Story: _____ Page: _____

What do all the sentences tell about? _____

_____

What is the main idea of the paragraph? _____

_____

Story: _____ Page: _____

What do all the sentences tell about? _____

_____

What is the main idea of the paragraph? _____

_____

Writing Paragraphs

Giving Facts

Authors of nonfiction give important facts to tell the reader about what happens. Find sentences in the story you have just read, or in other stories, that give important facts about what happens.

Story: _____ Page: _____

Important facts: _____

_____

_____

_____

Story: _____ Page: _____

Important facts: _____

_____

_____

_____

Story: _____ Page: _____

Important facts: _____

_____

_____

_____

Elaboration

Name

Using Words to Show Place

In this story, or in any other story you have read, find words that show place. Write the name of the story, the page number, and the word or group of words.

Story: _____ Page: _____

Words that show place: _____

_____

Story: _____ Page: _____

Words that show place: _____

_____

Story: _____ Page: _____

Words that show place: _____

_____

Story: _____ Page: _____

Words that show place: _____

_____

Use this page when you want to make your own writing better by using words that show place.

Name

Indicators of Place and Location

Giving Causes

Find a part in "James Forten, Hero and True Friend," or in other stories you have read, in which the author gives causes to tell why a character feels a certain way or to tell why something happens.

Story: _____ Page: _____

How does the character feel? _____

_____

_____

What caused the character to feel this way? _____

_____

_____

What happened? _____

_____

_____

What caused this to happen? _____

_____

_____

On another sheet of paper, answer these questions for another story you have read.

Cause and Effect

Name

Dialogue

Adding dialogue, or the exact words characters say, to a story helps the characters come alive. Look at *Buttons for General Washington*, or at other stories you have read to find examples of dialogue. Write what the speaker tag tells you about how the speaker is saying something.

Story: _____ Page: _____

Example of dialogue: _____

_____

_____

What does the speaker tag tell you? _____

_____

Story: _____ Page: _____

Example of dialogue: _____

_____

_____

What does the speaker tag tell you? _____

_____

Use this page when you want to use dialogue in your own writing.

Name

Expressing Characters' Thoughts and Feelings

Authors tell about their characters in many ways. In this story, or in any other story you have read, find examples of how the author lets you know the characters' thoughts and feelings.

Story: _____ Page: _____

Example of how the author lets you know characters' thoughts and feelings:

_____

_____

_____

Story: _____ Page: _____

Example of how the author lets you know characters' thoughts and feelings:

_____

_____

_____

Story: _____ Page: _____

Example of how the author lets you know characters' thoughts and feelings:

_____

_____

_____

Use this page when you want to show a character's thoughts and feelings in your own writing.

Characterization

Name

Giving Descriptions

Find examples in *The Pioneers*, or in any other stories you have read, in which the author gives descriptions to help the reader picture an idea.

Story: _____ Page: _____

What is being described? _____

_____

Description: _____

_____

_____

Story: _____ Page: _____

What is being described? _____

_____

Description: _____

_____

_____

Story: _____ Page: _____

What is being described? _____

_____

Description: _____

_____

_____

Elaboration

Giving Examples

Find parts in *The Pioneers*, or any other stories you
have read, in which the writer gives examples to make
an idea clear.

Story: _____ Page: _____

An idea that is made clear: _____

_____

_____

The sentence that gives an example to help make the idea clear:

_____

_____

Story: _____ Page: _____

An idea that is made clear: _____

_____

_____

The sentence that gives an example to help make the idea clear:

_____

_____

Look through the stories in your writing folder. See
if any of your writing needs to be revised by adding
examples.

Name

Elaboration

Informational Article

List other articles you have read. Write what each article is about. Then write some important facts that were in the article.

Article: _____

What is the article about? _____

Important facts: _____

_____

_____

Article: _____

What is the article about? _____

Important facts: _____

_____

_____

Article: _____

What is the article about? _____

Important facts: _____

_____

_____

Giving Reasons

Find examples in "Out of Many People, One Nation," or in any other stories you have read, in which the author gives reasons to explain why events happened or why things are the way they are. For each example write the situation or the event. Then write the reasons the author gives for it. Use your own words.

Story: _____ Page: _____

Situation or event: _____

_____

Reason or reasons given for the situation or event: _____

_____

_____

_____

Story: _____ Page: _____

Situation or event: _____

_____

Reason or reasons given for the situation or event: _____

_____

_____

_____

Name

Elaboration

Our Country: *E Pluribus Unum*/Unit 8

Using Words to Show Time, Order, and Place

Look through *Abraham Lincoln* or other stories you
have read for words used to show time, order, and
place. Write the name of the story, the signal word or
words, and what they show (time, order, or place).

Story	Signal Word or Words	What They Show

Indicators of Time, Order, and Place

Name

Characterization

Writers use many ways to make their characters interesting and believable. Find examples from *Abraham Lincoln* or from any other stories you have read in which the author *tells* about a character or *shows* a character's actions to help you know a character better.

Story: _____ Page: _____

Does the author *tell* about a character or *show* a character's actions?

_____

What do you know about the character from this example? _____

_____

_____

Story: _____ Page: _____

Does the author *tell* about a character or *show* a character's actions?

_____

What do you know about the character from this example? _____

_____

_____

Refer to this page when you want to show or tell about a character's actions in your own writing.

Name

Giving Definitions

Writers sometimes include in the story the meanings of words that may be hard for a reader to understand. In "La Florida" or in any other story that you have read, find definitions.

Story: _____ Page: _____

Word (or phrase) that is defined: _____

_____

Definition that is given: _____

_____

_____

_____

Story: _____ Page: _____

Word (or phrase) that is defined: _____

_____

Definition that is given: _____

_____

_____

_____

Name _____

Elaboration

Descriptions

In "East Meets West," the author gives descriptions
to help the reader form a clear picture of a place or an
event. In this story or in others that you have read,
find descriptions that help you picture a place or event.
Write them on the lines below.

Story: _____ Page: _____

Sentence with description: _____

_____

_____

Story: _____ Page: _____

Sentence with description: _____

_____

_____

Story: _____ Page: _____

Sentence with description: _____

_____

_____

Use this page when you want to use description in
your writing to make your ideas clear.

Elaboration

Using Quotations

Look through *Martin Luther King, Jr.*, or other real-life stories that you have read in which the author uses quotations. Write the name of the story, the page number, the quotation, and the name of the person who wrote or spoke the words.

Story: _____ Page: _____

Quotation: _____

_____

Person who wrote or spoke the words: _____

Story: _____ Page: _____

Quotation: _____

_____

Person who wrote or spoke the words: _____

Story: _____ Page: _____

Quotation: _____

_____

Person who wrote or spoke the words: _____

Look through your writing folder to see whether any piece of your writing could be improved by adding quotations.

Elaboration

Giving Information About an Event

In *Martin Luther King, Jr.*, the author gives important facts about events that were to lead to many changes in our country. Find sentences in this story or in other stories that you have read in which the author gives important facts about an event.

Story: _____ Page: _____

Important facts: _____

_____

_____

_____

Story: _____ Page: _____

Important facts: _____

_____

_____

_____

Story: _____ Page: _____

Important facts: _____

_____

_____

_____

Name

Elaboration

Our Country: *E Pluribus Unum*/Unit 8

PHASES IN THE WRITING PROCESS

Prewriting

Drafting

Revising

Proofreading

Publishing

Being a Writer

Good writers think about their writing. They think about *what* they want to say—their purpose in writing. They think about *how* they want to say it—their organization, their method of presentation, their vocabulary. They think about *who* will be reading it—young children, older children, teenagers, adults, experts—and consider whether their audience will find the writing interesting and easy to understand.

On the pages following are charts of writers' major purposes such as: to tell a story, to describe something, to persuade, or to inform. These major purposes are often called modes of discourse or writing domains.

Purpose for Writing	Points to Keep in Mind When Writing	Types of Writing Used for This Purpose
To Tell a Story (a narrative) • fiction—the writer makes up all or most of the story • nonfiction—the writer tells a story that has actually happened to the writer or to others	A good story has • a beginning that grabs the reader's attention • a middle that contains story events that build to a climax • an ending that leaves the reader satisfied	*folk tales* fairy tales, fables, myths, legends, tall tales *fantasies* animal fantasies, science fiction *mysteries* *adventure tales* *humorous stories* *realistic fiction* stories that seem real *biography* real life of a person *autobiography* real life of the writer

Being a Writer *continued*

In many pieces of writing, the author has a single purpose; in some, the writer may have more than one. For example, in the review of a book that you want to persuade your classmates to read, you will also tell them what the book is about.

The points listed in column 2, Points to Keep in Mind When Writing, can help you be a better writer and achieve your purpose. You may wish to experiment with some of the different types of writing listed in column 3, Types of Writing Used for This Purpose. The anthology selections listed in column 4 show how good writers have achieved their various purposes.

Examples from Your Anthology (in order, by unit; some titles are shortened)	Your Notes and Ideas
Folk Tales — (1) *The Hole in the Dike; The Legend of the Bluebonnet* (2) The Three Wishes; The Goose That Laid the Golden Eggs; *The Empty Pot; Cinderella;* The Golden Goose (4) *The Elves and the Shoemaker;* The Camel's Nose; The North Wind and the Sun (5) The Boy Who Cried Wolf; The Grasshopper and the Ants (6) The Foolish, Timid Rabbit; The Fox and the Crow; *The Emperor's New Clothes* **Fantasies** — (1) Dragons and Giants (2) *The Simple Prince* (3) *The Dinosaur Who Lived in My Backyard* (4) *Mushroom in the Rain; Corduroy* (5) *The Tale of Peter Rabbit* **Realistic Fiction** — (1) *Molly the Brave and Me* (4) *Music, Music for Everyone* (5) *A Pair of Red Clogs; The Pudding Like a Night on the Sea* (6) *Crow Boy* (8) *Watch the Stars Come Out* **Historical Fiction** — (7) *Buttons for General Washington* **Biography** — (1) *Sally Ride, Astronaut* (4) *Clara Barton* (7) *Follow the Dream* (8) *Abraham Lincoln; Martin Luther King, Jr.*	_____ _____ _____ _____ _____ _____ _____ _____ _____ _____ _____

Purpose for Writing	Points to Keep in Mind When Writing	Types of Writing Used for this Purpose
To Describe • a person or animal • a place • an object • an event or experience • thoughts and feelings	• Get the reader to see or feel the thing being described. • Be clear. Give details. Use vivid words. • Use sensory language— words that help the reader see, hear, smell, taste, touch the thing being described.	Character sketches (portraits in words) Descriptive essays Photo essays (written descriptions accompanied by photographs) Poetry Journal or diary entries Personal letters Greeting cards
To Persuade	• Support all opinions with facts. • Give convincing reasons. Avoid weak reasons. • Present reasons in a logical order (start with strongest reason).	Opinion essays Reviews (books, films) Newspaper editorials (writer expresses view on important issue) Letters to the editor (reader gives opinions) Speeches Advertisements
To Inform (expository or informational text) • important information that someone needs to know (messages, announcements) • information on a topic • information that explains how something works (as in a diagram) • information that explains how to do or make something (as in a recipe)	• Your reader should understand and remember the information. • Arrange the information to make it easy to understand and remember. • Concentrate on causes and effects. • Concentrate on the sequence of events. • Concentrate on comparing and contrasting. • Put information in logical order.	Research reports News reports or articles Magazine articles Business letters Directions Recipes Invitations Announcements Telephone messages Charts Diagrams

Examples from Your Anthology (in order, by unit; some titles are shortened)	Your Notes and Ideas
(1) *Sally Ride, Astronaut* **(3)** Fossils; Iguanadon; Seismosaurus **(6)** Waking; Who Has Seen the Wind?; An Emerald Is as Green as Grass **(8)** Indian Children of Long Ago; Buffalo Dusk	_____ _____ _____ _____ _____
(none)	_____ _____ _____ _____ _____
(2) Amadou's Story **(3)** *Fossils Tell of Long Ago*; Why Did the Dinosaurs Disappear?; Monster Tracks **(5)** Three Hundred Spartans **(6)** *How We Learned the Earth Is Round* **(7)** *The First Americans*; Squanto and the First Thanksgiving; James Forten, Hero and True Friend; The First Fourth of July; *The Pioneers* **(8)** Out of Many People, One Nation; La Florida; East Meets West	_____ _____ _____ _____ _____ _____ _____ _____ _____

SETTING READING GOALS AND EXPECTATIONS

Reading Strategies	Ask Yourself
ACTIVATE prior knowledge.	What do I already know about this?
BROWSE the text.	What kind of text is this? What looks interesting? What might cause problems?
CONSIDER why you are reading.	Am I reading this for fun? Am I reading this to learn something? What do I want to learn?
DECIDE WHAT you expect from the text.	What might this be about? What do I want to find out?

RESPONDING TO TEXT

Reading Strategies	Ask Yourself
MAKE CONNECTIONS between what you are reading and what you already know.	What does this remind me of?
VISUALIZE OR PICTURE what is happening in the text.	Can I picture in my mind what is described in the text? Would a drawing help me understand the text?
WONDER freely as you read.	I wonder why this is the way it is? I wonder what else there is to know about this?
PREDICT what will happen next.	What did I already know that helped me predict? Which pictures helped me predict?
THINK ABOUT how the text makes you feel.	How do I feel about what I'm reading?

CHECKING UNDERSTANDING

Reading Strategies

INTERPRET as you read.

SUM UP to check your
understanding as you read.

ASK QUESTIONS to check your
understanding as you read.

Ask Yourself

What does the text mean?

Does this make sense?
What is this section about?
What is the whole selection about?
Can I find out more if I look back?

What could my teacher ask here?
What could be on a test?

Clarifying Unfamiliar Words and Passages

Reading Strategies	**Ask Yourself**
Apply decoding skills if there are unknown words.	Have I seen this word before? What words that I already know are like this word? Can I sound this out? Can I break this long word into parts? What small words in the long word will help me read it?
Determine what is unclear.	Do I understand the meanings of all the words? Which parts are unclear? How can I make sense of them?
Apply context clues if there are words whose meanings you don't know.	What context clues can I find in the rest of the sentence or in the sentences around the word?
Check the dictionary.	
Reread the passage that didn't make sense to you.	Does the passage make sense now?

PLANNING AND SETTING WRITING GOALS

Writing Strategies	**Ask Yourself**
USE READING to improve your writing.	What did this author do that I really liked? How can I do this in my writing?
RECORD interesting and important topics to write about.	What is important or interesting to me and others? Did something happen to me that I'd like to share?
NOTE information you will need in order to write.	What are the important ideas that I want others to know about this? What do I already know? What will I need to know?
DECIDE on the main goals of the writing.	What is my purpose for writing this? What are the important points that I want to get across?
REVISE your plans.	Have my writing ideas changed after thinking about my topic? How?

CONSIDERING READERS

Writing Strategies	**Ask Yourself**
MAKE your topic interesting.	Will others be interested in this? What can I do or add to make this topic more interesting to others?
DECIDE what effect you want to have on your readers.	Who am I writing for? How do I want to make readers feel? What do I want readers to learn?
DETERMINE if readers will understand.	Will readers understand this? Is there enough information? If not, what can I add? Is it clear and well written?
PREDICT your readers' reactions, and then compare their reactions to what you expected.	If readers don't know anything about this topic, will they enjoy reading this? If they are reading this for the first time, what might they say about the topic? Was I right?
SUMMARIZE audience reactions.	Did many readers have the same comments? What were they? What is good about my composition? What do I need to change?

REVISING CONTENT

Writing Strategies	Ask Yourself
REREAD very carefully.	Have I left out words or put in unnecessary words? Does my writing make sense?
PINPOINT parts of your composition that can be made clearer.	Is this descriptive enough for readers to picture?
IDENTIFY information confusing to readers.	Were my readers confused? Could this information be wrong? How can I check and correct it?
REORGANIZE IDEAS OR INFORMATION.	What's my purpose for writing this? Am I achieving that purpose? Do I need to include more facts? Do I need to take out any unnecessary information?
USE A STORY FRAME OR PLOT LINE.	Who are the main characters? What is the problem? What are the story events? Are there conflicts or blocks? Does my story build to a high point? Does the story come to a satisfactory conclusion? Would dialogue help to develop my story?
CONSIDER YOUR OWN REACTIONS AND IDEAS.	How do I feel about my writing? Am I pleased with my writing? Did I include all the information I had planned? What would I like to change?